VM5S
Student Edition

Ronald Slabbinck and Holly Shaw-Slabbinck

ONE-MINUTE THEORY

Book One

Name _____

Folder # _____

Ensemble _____

KJOS Neil A. Kjos Music Company, *Publisher*

TABLE OF CONTENTS

ISBN 0-8497-4205-6

Ron Slabbinck and **Holly Shaw-Slabbinck** teach at Christian Brothers High School in Sacramento, California, where they reside with their two children.

They both hold undergraduate degrees in Music Education from Western Michigan University. Ron completed his Master's Degree in Conducting at California State University, Sacramento, under the direction of Dr. Donald Kendrick. Holly holds a Master's Degree in Mental Health Counseling from the University of Central Florida.

Prior to teaching, Ron and Holly were professional singers. Their experiences range from singing in the *Voices of Liberty* at Epcot Center at Disney World, to performing on Carnival Cruise Lines, as well as performing at a number of theme parks around the country. Holly's voice can also be heard on various studio recordings, including those of her father, Kirby Shaw.

Before moving to California, Ron and Holly team-taught a high school choral music program that included seven ensembles, two piano classes, and a music theory class.

Both Ron and Holly have been regular vocal clinicians for *Showchoir Camps of America*, have adjudicated festivals throughout the country, and continue to promote quality choral education.

Also available:
One Minute Theory, Book Two
Student Edition   (VM11S)
Test Bank   (VM11T)

Unit 1

Date: / /

We know an age more vividly through its music than its historians.
Rosanne Ambrose-Brown

In order to understand music in its written form, the first step is to recognize the basic STAFF. A STAFF is a group of five equally spaced horizontal lines upon which music is written.

Use the dots below as guides to draw three STAVES (plural for STAFF):

Date: / /

*Music expresses that which cannot be said and
on which it is impossible to be silent.*

Victor Hugo

Define STAFF and then draw three STAVES below:

STAFF _____

_____

Date: / /

Music may achieve the highest of all missions: she may be a bond between nations, races, and states, who are strangers to one another in many ways; she may unite what is disunited, and bring peace to what is hostile.

Dr. Max Bendiner

At the beginning of every STAFF is a symbol that helps us identify musical notes and pitches. This symbol is called a CLEF. One of the most common clefs is the TREBLE CLEF, also known as the G CLEF.

A TREBLE CLEF (G CLEF) looks like this on the staff:

Practice drawing a TREBLE CLEF below:

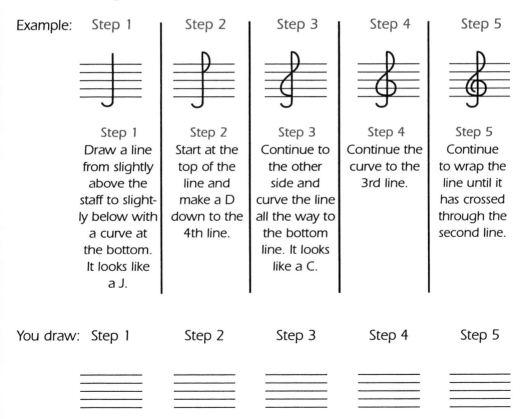

Example: Step 1 | Step 2 | Step 3 | Step 4 | Step 5

Step 1: Draw a line from slightly above the staff to slightly below with a curve at the bottom. It looks like a J.

Step 2: Start at the top of the line and make a D down to the 4th line.

Step 3: Continue to the other side and curve the line all the way to the bottom line. It looks like a C.

Step 4: Continue the curve to the 3rd line.

Step 5: Continue to wrap the line until it has crossed through the second line.

You draw: Step 1   Step 2   Step 3   Step 4   Step 5

Date: /   /

*Giving to others selflessly and anonymously, radiating light throughout
the world and illuminating your own darkness, your virtue becomes
a sanctuary for yourself and all beings.*

Lao-tsu

It is important to place the TREBLE CLEF exactly as it is seen below. Following
the examples shown, draw five TREBLE CLEFS on each STAFF:

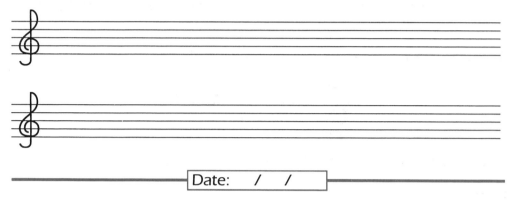

Date: /   /

*Through music we may wander where we will in time, and
find friends in every century.*

Helen Thomson

Another common CLEF is the BASS CLEF, also known as the F CLEF. A BASS
CLEF (F CLEF) drawn on a STAFF looks like this:

Example: Step 1   Step 2

Step 1   Step 2
Draw what looks like a   Place dots on either side
large quotation mark: of the 4th line.
starting with a dot on the 4th
line, touch the top line, and
go to just below the 2nd line.

You draw: Step 1   Step 2

Date: / /

It is one of the most beautiful compensations of this life that no man can sincerely try to help another without helping himself.

Ralph Waldo Emerson

It is important to place the BASS CLEF exactly as it is seen below. Following the examples shown, draw five BASS CLEFS on each STAFF:

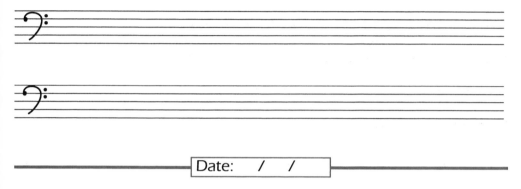

Date: / /

*Happiness is when what you think,
what you say, and what you do are in harmony.*

Mahatma Gandhi

Draw five TREBLE CLEFS and BASS CLEFS on each STAFF:

VM5S

Date: / /

Give a man a fish; you have fed him for today.
Teach a man to fish; you have fed him for a lifetime.

Chinese Proverb

In music, there are symbols called NOTES that represent the length of sound.

Each written note has a letter name. Once you know the letter names of notes, you will be able to read music. It is easy to remember the music alphabet because it is the first seven letters of our regular alphabet.

Write the following sentence three times:

The music alphabet is A B C D E F G.

_____

_____

_____

Select your favorite daily quote from the quotes you have read and write it below:

_____

_____

_____

_____

_____

Date: / /

True compassion is more than flinging a coin at a beggar;
it comes to see that an edifice which produces beggars needs restructuring.
Rev. Dr. Martin Luther King, Jr.

Each line and space on a STAFF is assigned a specific letter from the music alphabet. The CLEF determines placement of each letter.

Use the example below as a reference:

Line 5
Space 4
Line 4
Space 3
Line 3
Space 2
Line 2
Space 1
Line 1

The TREBLE or G CLEF tells us where the letter G is on the STAFF. Notice that the G CLEF curls around the 2nd LINE of the STAFF. This means that LINE 2 in TREBLE or G CLEF is the letter G.

Draw six TREBLE or G CLEFS and complete the inner curl so that it includes the G line:

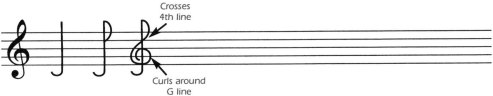

The BASS or F CLEF tells us where the letter F is on the STAFF. Notice that the two dots on the F CLEF surround the 4th LINE. This means that LINE 4 in BASS or F CLEF is the letter F.

Draw six BASS or F CLEFS, making sure that the two dots are on either side of the F LINE:

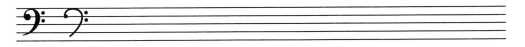

Date: / /

When you do the common things in life in an unknown way,
you will command the attention of the world.

George Washington Carver

Once you have identified the 2nd LINE in TREBLE or G CLEF as a G, it is simple to name the rest of the lines and spaces. All you need to do is alternate LINE-SPACE-LINE.

Go forward through the music alphabet when you go up, and go backward through the music alphabet when you go down. When you run out of letters (A-G), repeat the sequence.

Using the example below, finish writing the letter names for each line and SPACE on the STAFF:

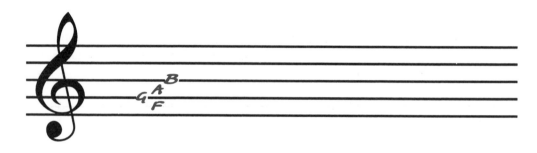

Date: / /

In order to remember the names of the LINES in the TREBLE CLEF, it is helpful to memorize a sentence as a reference. Look at the LINES in the TREBLE CLEF. From bottom to top the note names are E G B D F. The sentence "Every Good Boy Does Fine" can help you remember the names of the LINES of the TREBLE CLEF.

Write the sentence "Every Good Boy Does Fine" below:

_____

There are many other sentences you can create to remind yourself of the LINES in TREBLE or G CLEF.

Some examples are:
Elvis' Guitar Broke Down Friday

or

Elephants Go Bouncing Down Freeways

On the line below, create your own sentence to remind you of the letter names of the LINES in TREBLE CLEF:

_____

Write the letter name of each TREBLE CLEF LINE below the appropriate notes:

___ ___ ___ ___ ___

Date: / /

Life is either a daring adventure, or it is nothing.

Helen Keller

Just like the lines in the TREBLE CLEF, the SPACES can also be remembered easily, because they spell the word FACE.

Write the following sentence three times:

The spaces in the TREBLE CLEF from bottom to top spell the word FACE.

_____

_____

_____

For the example below, write the letter name of each TREBLE CLEF SPACE below the appropriate notes:

—————   —————   —————   —————

Date: / /

No one can make you feel inferior without your permission.

Eleanor Roosevelt

Below are several notes placed on the TREBLE STAFF.

If the circle is completely between two lines, it is considered a SPACE NOTE and is assigned the letter of the SPACE that it covers.

If the circle has a line going through the middle of it, it is considered a LINE NOTE and is assigned the letter of the LINE that goes through it.

Write the correct letter name below each note:

A __ __ __ __ __ __ __

Date: /   /

There might be some people who can stop you temporarily, but you are the only one who can do it permanently.

Anonymous

Write the notes on the STAFF that correspond with the letter names below. For SPACES, neatly draw a circle that is contained between two lines. For LINES, neatly draw the circle, making sure the line runs directly through the center of the circle.

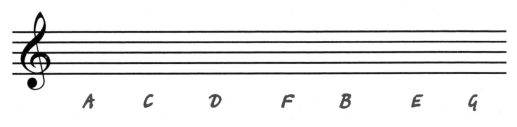

A   C   D   F   B   E   G

Select your favorite daily quote and put it into your own words:

_____

_____

_____

_____

Date: /   /

People usually say, "The sky is the limit." I believe the sky is just the beginning.

Unknown

Once you have identified the FOURTH LINE in BASS or F CLEF to be an F, it is simple to name the rest of the LINES and SPACES. All you need to do is alternate LINE-SPACE-LINE.

Go forward through the music alphabet when you go up, and backward through the music alphabet when you go down. When you run out of letters (A-G), repeat the sequence.

Using the example below, finish writing the letter names for each LINE and SPACE on the STAFF:

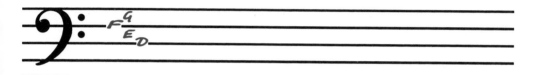

Date: /   /

If I think I can do it, I know I can. If I know I can, then I will.

Unknown

In order to remember the names of the LINES in the BASS CLEF, it is helpful to memorize a sentence as a reference. Look at the LINES in the BASS CLEF. From bottom to top the note names are G B D F A. The sentence "Good Boys Do Fine Always" can help you remember the names of the LINES of the BASS CLEF.

Write the sentence "Good Boys Do Fine Always" below:

_____

There are many other sentences that you can create to remind yourself of the LINES in BASS CLEF.

One example is:
                        Great Big Dreams For America

On the line below, create your own sentence to remind you of the letter names of the LINES in BASS or F CLEF:

_____

Write the letter name of each BASS CLEF LINE below the appropriate note:

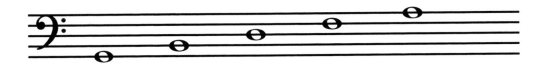

___   ___   ___   ___   ___

If people are not humane, what is the use of rites?
If people are not humane, what is the use of music?

Confucius

Look at the SPACES in the BASS CLEF. From bottom to top the note names are
A C E G. The sentence "All Cows Eat Grass" can help you remember the names
of the SPACES in the BASS CLEF.

Write the sentence "All Cows Eat Grass" below:

_____

Try to come up with another sentence for the SPACES in BASS CLEF:

_____

Write the letter name of each BASS CLEF SPACE below the appropriate note:

___   ___   ___   ___

Date: /   /

No dreamer is ever too small; no dream is ever too big.

Unknown

Remember that a SPACE NOTE is completely between two lines, and a LINE NOTE has a line going through the middle of it.

Below are several notes written on the STAFF.

Below each note, write the correct letter name:

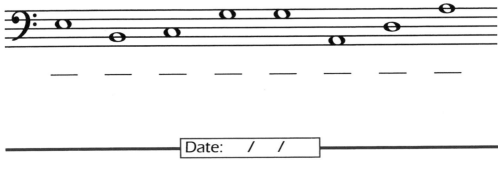

Date: /   /

For it is in giving that we receive.

Saint Francis of Assisi

Below are a number of notes written in TREBLE CLEF and BASS CLEF. Write the corresponding letter names on the lines provided:

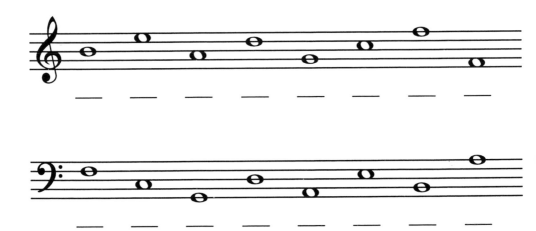

Date: / /

Whatever is good to know is difficult to learn.

Greek Proverb

QUIZ 1 REVIEW

Write the definition of STAFF:

_____

_____

The symbol below is called a _____ or _____ .

Write the correct letter name below each note:

The symbol below is called a _____ or _____ .

Write the correct letter name below each note:

VM5S

Unit 2

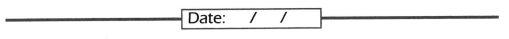

Date: /   /

Honesty is the first chapter in the book of wisdom.

Thomas Jefferson

In addition to using LINES and SPACES to determine how high or low a note should sound, you will use WHOLE NOTES, HALF NOTES, QUARTER NOTES, and EIGHTH NOTES to determine how long a note should sound.

Below you will see a breakdown of the note durations:

Term	Symbol	Rhythmic Duration
Whole Note	𝅝	4 beats
Half Note	𝅗𝅥	2 beats
Quarter Note	♩	1 beat
Two Eighth Notes	♫ or ♪♪	1 beat

When two EIGHTH NOTES appear together, they often look like this: ♫

A single EIGHTH NOTE is written with a FLAG instead of the connecting beam: ♪

Using the chart above, complete the mathematical exercises below:

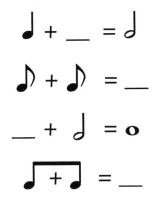

♩ + __ = 𝅗𝅥

♪ + ♪ = __

__ + 𝅗𝅥 = 𝅝

♫ + ♩ = __

Date: /   /

If you do the same thing over and over again, you cannot ever expect a different outcome.

Albert Einstein

Below is a breakdown of four common rhythmic values:

Whole Note

Half Notes

Quarter Notes

Eighth Notes

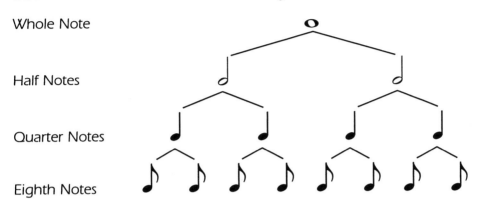

Of the notes above, the EIGHTH NOTE is the shortest in duration.

It takes two EIGHTH NOTES to equal one QUARTER NOTE.

It takes two QUARTER NOTES to equal one HALF NOTE.

It takes two HALF NOTES to equal one WHOLE NOTE.

Answer the following questions:

How many HALF NOTES does it take to equal a WHOLE NOTE? _____

How many QUARTER NOTES does it take to equal a HALF NOTE? _____

How many EIGHTH NOTES does it take to equal a QUARTER NOTE? _____

Date: /   /

Real champions believe in themselves even when no one else will!

Unknown

A QUARTER NOTE is made up of a STEM and a NOTE HEAD.

If the STEM goes up, it is placed on the right side of the NOTE HEAD.

If the STEM goes down, it is placed on the left side of the NOTE HEAD.

Any note below the third line needs an UP STEM.

Any note on or above the third line needs a DOWN STEM.

The following are QUARTER NOTES:

Practice drawing QUARTER NOTES below, making sure that the STEM is the correct direction based on the examples above:

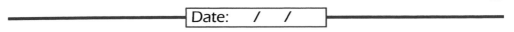

Consideration for others is the basis of a good life, a good society.

Confucius

A HALF NOTE is also made up of a STEM and a NOTE HEAD.

The following are HALF NOTES:

Practice drawing HALF NOTES below, making sure that the STEM is the correct direction based on the examples above:

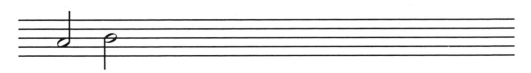

24

When you feel the muscles in your shoulders straining, when your heart is beating two-hundred times a minute, when your legs feel like they can't handle one more turn, and when each breath burns your lungs, that's when you know you have to push harder.

Unknown

A WHOLE NOTE consists only of a NOTE HEAD and looks like this:

O

The following are WHOLE NOTES:

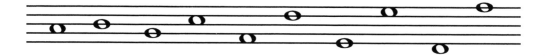

Practice drawing WHOLE NOTES below:

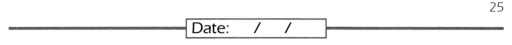

Don't find fault; find a remedy.

Henry Ford

When two EIGHTH NOTES appear together, they have something more than the STEM and NOTE HEAD. They are linked together by a BEAM.

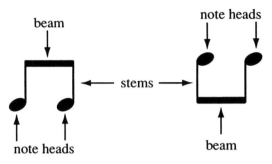

A single EIGHTH NOTE has something different in addition to the STEM and NOTE HEAD. There is a FLAG on the top or bottom of the STEM.

The following are EIGHTH NOTES:

Practice drawing EIGHTH NOTES below, making sure that the STEMS are the correct length and that the FLAGS or BEAMS are accurately drawn based on the examples above:

| Date: / / |

Our doubts are traitors, and make us lose the good we oft would win,
by fearing to attempt.

William Shakespeare

As you have learned, in music there are symbols (NOTES) that represent the length of sound.

There are also symbols that represent the length of no sound, which are called RESTS.

RESTS that you will use include WHOLE, HALF, QUARTER, and EIGHTH RESTS.

Below you will see a breakdown of the REST durations:

Term	Symbol	Rhythmic Duration	Note Equivalent
Whole Rest	▬	4 beats	𝅝
Half Rest	▬	2 beats	𝅗𝅥
Quarter Rest	𝄽	1 beat	𝅘𝅥
Eighth Rest	𝄾	½ beat	𝅘𝅥𝅮

Using the chart above, complete the mathematical exercises below:

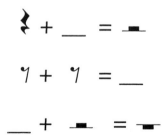

$$𝄽 + \underline{} = ▬$$

$$𝄾 + 𝄾 = \underline{}$$

$$\underline{} + ▬ = ▬$$

Date: / /

The direction we are facing determines our destination.

Unknown

Below is a breakdown of four common rhythmic values:

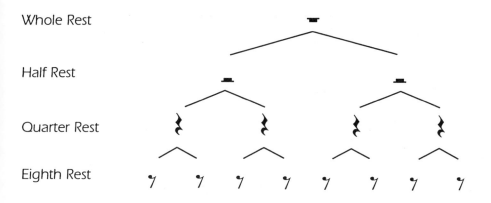

Whole Rest

Half Rest

Quarter Rest

Eighth Rest

Of the four RESTS, the EIGHTH REST is the shortest.

It takes two EIGHTH RESTS to equal one QUARTER REST.

It takes two QUARTER RESTS to equal one HALF REST.

It takes two HALF RESTS to equal one WHOLE REST.

Answer the following questions:

How many HALF RESTS does it take to equal a WHOLE REST? _____

How many QUARTER RESTS does it take to equal a HALF REST?_____

How many EIGHTH RESTS does it take to equal a QUARTER REST? _____

Date: /   /

Wisdom does not come from knowing all, but from knowing that there is still something to be learned.

Unknown

The following are EIGHTH RESTS:

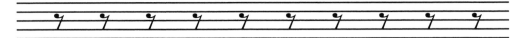

Practice drawing EIGHTH RESTS below:

How many EIGHTH RESTS does it take to equal a WHOLE REST? _____

How many EIGHTH RESTS does it take to equal a HALF REST? _____

Date: /   /

The secret of success is for a person to be ready when his opportunity comes.

Benjamin Disraeli

The following are QUARTER RESTS:

Practice drawing QUARTER RESTS below:

How many QUARTER RESTS does it take to equal a WHOLE REST? _____

How many QUARTER RESTS does it take to equal a HALF REST? _____

Date: /   /

Respond intelligently even to unintelligent treatment.

Lao-Tsu

The following are HALF RESTS:

Practice drawing HALF RESTS below:

How many HALF RESTS does it take to equal one WHOLE REST? _____

How many QUARTER RESTS does it take to equal a HALF REST?   _____

Date: /   /

Life's most persistent and urgent question is, 'What are you doing for others?'
Rev. Dr. Martin Luther King, Jr.

The following are WHOLE RESTS:

Practice drawing WHOLE RESTS below:

Notice the difference between a HALF REST and a WHOLE REST. A WHOLE REST looks like an upside down hat in which the REST itself hangs below the 4th LINE (the rim of the hat). A HALF REST looks like a right-side up hat in which the REST sits on top of the 3rd LINE (the rim of the hat).

Think of a man wearing a top hat. If he takes his hat off (WHOLE REST) he is a whole gentleman. If, however, he leaves his hat on (HALF REST), he is only half a gentleman.

Date: / /

Unless you do something beyond what you have already mastered, you will never grow.

Ralph Waldo Emerson

Quiz 2 Review

Based on the example shown, solve the following equations:

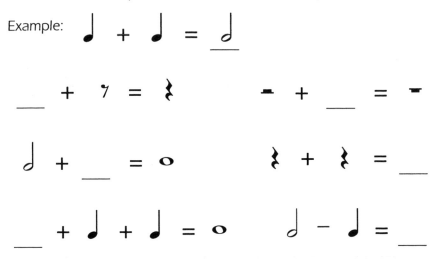

Below each note, write the correct letter name:

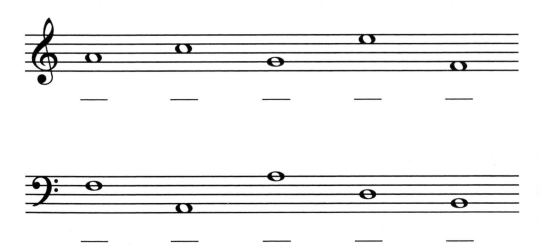

Unit 3

Human kindness has never weakened the stamina or softened the fiber of a free people. A nation does not have to be cruel in order to be tough.

Franklin Delano Roosevelt

When a STAFF with a TREBLE CLEF and a STAFF with a BASS CLEF are grouped together they are called a GRAND STAFF.

Usually, piano players read a GRAND STAFF. The TREBLE STAFF is commonly used for the right hand, and the BASS STAFF is commonly used for the left hand.

A GRAND STAFF is grouped together using a BRACE that is placed to the left of the two STAVES. The GRAND STAFF is shown below:

Complete each GRAND STAFF below including the BRACE, TREBLE CLEF, and BASS CLEF:

Learn from your mistakes so that you may teach others what you have learned.
Unknown

SOPRANOS (S) read the notes on the TREBLE STAFF that are either on the top, or that have STEMS going up.

ALTOS (A) read the notes on the TREBLE STAFF that are either on the bottom, or that have STEMS going down.

TENORS (T) read the notes on the BASS STAFF that are either on the top, or that have STEMS going up.

BASSES (B) read the notes on the BASS STAFF that are either on the bottom, or that have STEMS going down.

Example:

On the GRAND STAFF below, indicate whether the note shown or indicated would be sung by SOPRANO (S), ALTO (A), TENOR (T), or BASS (B):

VM5S

Date: / /

The world is moved along, not only by the mighty shoves of its heroes, but also by the aggregate of tiny pushes of each honest worker.

Helen Keller

The GRAND STAFF is often used for SATB chorus, but it is also common for each voice part to be assigned its own STAFF. In music, the STAVES are organized from the highest voices on top to the lowest voices on the bottom. The order from top to bottom is SOPRANO, ALTO, TENOR, and BASS. This means that there will be FOUR STAVES grouped together with a BRACKET.

Write the voice part that goes with each STAFF on the left side:

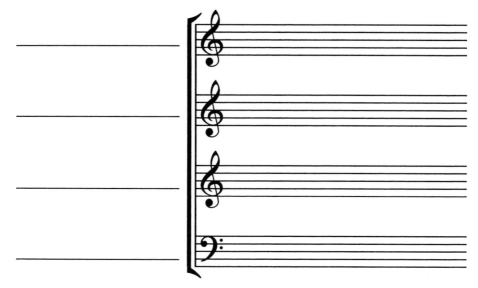

In female ensembles, the STAVES will generally be organized from top to bottom in the order of SOPRANO I, SOPRANO II, and ALTO. Write the voice part for each part on the left side:

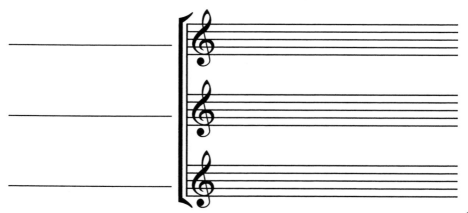

Date: /   /

When all the people in the world love one another, then the strong
will not overpower the weak, the many will not oppress the few,
the wealthy will not mock the poor, the honored will not disdain the humble,
and the cunning will not deceive the simple.

Motsi

In choral music, there will often be a GRAND STAFF assigned to the piano, and additional STAVES, grouped together with a BRACKET, for individual voice parts.

Write the appropriate word (SOPRANO, ALTO, TENOR, BASS, PIANO) to the left of each STAFF:

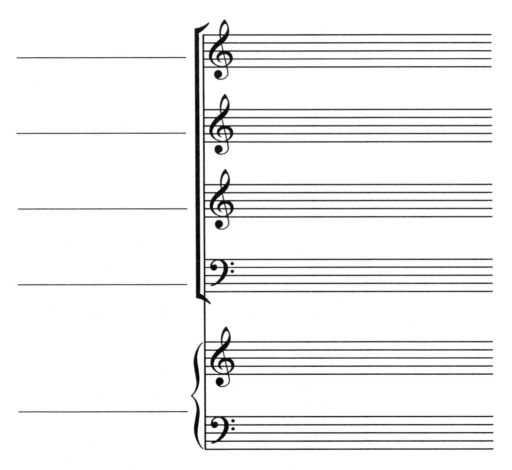

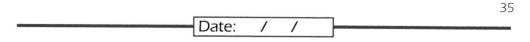

They can because they think they can.

Virgil

QUIZ 3 REVIEW

For the scores below, indicate which lines are to be sung by SOPRANO (S), ALTO (A), TENOR (T), BASS (B), and which are to be played on the PIANO.

Silent Night by Kirby Shaw
©1989 Kirby Shaw Music
Used with permission 2005

VM5S

Unit 4

Date: /   /

Believe that with your feelings and your work you are taking part in the greatest; the more strongly you cultivate this belief, the more will reality and the world go forth from it.

Rainer Maria Rilke

In music, notes are organized into equal groups called MEASURES. A MEASURE is the space within a STAFF contained between two BAR LINES.

Below is a STAFF indicating BAR LINES and MEASURES:

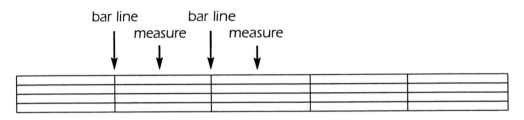

On the STAFF below, draw enough BAR LINES to make six MEASURES:

To get to the top of a tree is easy, but you have to climb up the tree first.

Unknown

At the beginning of each STAFF, to the right of the CLEF are two numbers that look like a fraction. These two numbers are called the TIME SIGNATURE.

Each number has its own meaning. The top number tells us how many beats are in each MEASURE. The bottom number tells us what kind of note receives one beat.

In the examples shown, the bottom number is 4.

4 represents a QUARTER NOTE.

What does the top number in a TIME SIGNATURE tell us? _____

_____

What does the bottom number in a TIME SIGNATURE tell us? _____

_____

Date: / /

An eye for an eye only ends up making the whole world blind.

Mahatma Gandhi

In a TIME SIGNATURE, the bottom number indicates what type of note receives one beat. In all of the examples below, one QUARTER NOTE equals one beat. However, there is a different number of beats in each MEASURE.

In $\frac{4}{4}$ there are 4 beats in each MEASURE, and the QUARTER NOTE gets one beat.

In $\frac{3}{4}$ there are 3 beats in each MEASURE, and the QUARTER NOTE gets one beat.

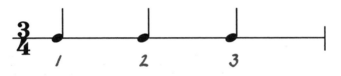

In $\frac{2}{4}$ there are 2 beats in each MEASURE, and the QUARTER NOTE gets one beat.

Below are three incomplete MEASURES. Using QUARTER NOTES, complete each MEASURE according to the TIME SIGNATURE:

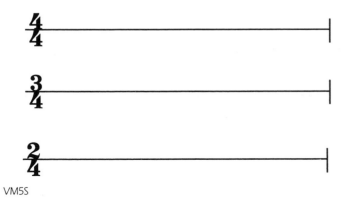

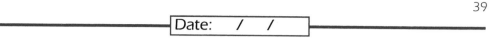

If I had six hours to cut down a tree, I would spend
four hours sharpening my axe!

Old Chinese Martial Arts Master

Once it has been determined how many beats are in each MEASURE, you can count each MEASURE according to the TIME SIGNATURE. For example, the following MEASURES in $\frac{4}{4}$ would be counted "1 2 3 4" in a rhythmic pattern:

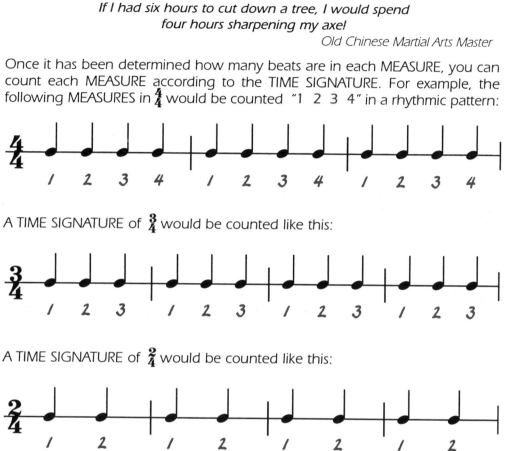

A TIME SIGNATURE of $\frac{3}{4}$ would be counted like this:

A TIME SIGNATURE of $\frac{2}{4}$ would be counted like this:

In each of the examples shown below, draw BAR LINES to create four complete MEASURES. Then complete each MEASURE using QUARTER NOTES and write the correct numbers for counting.

Date: / /

Compassion is the basis of all morality.

Arthur Schopenhauer

When writing numbers for counting, the longer notes must be accounted for by placing the correct beat number in parentheses.

Example:

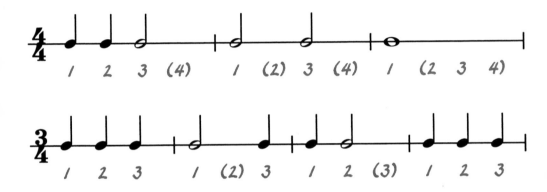

1   2   3   (4)   1   (2)   3   (4)   1   (2   3   4)

1   2   3   1   (2)   3   1   2   (3)   1   2   3

Write the correct counts under these notes:

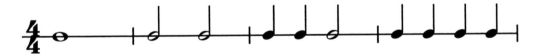

First bring peace within yourself, then you can also bring peace to others.
Thomas a' Kempis, German Monk

When you see a REST in music, you must be silent for the length of time it indicates. Therefore, when you count a REST, you need to allow for its duration. Do this by writing "**sh**" under the REST instead of a number.

Example:

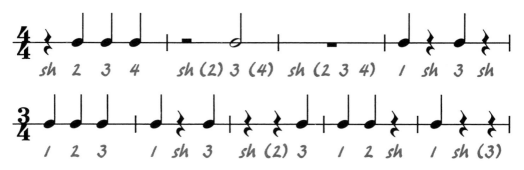

sh 2 3 4   sh (2) 3 (4) sh (2 3 4) / sh 3 sh

/ 2 3   / sh 3   sh (2) 3   / 2 sh   / sh (3)

Write the correct counts for the examples shown below:

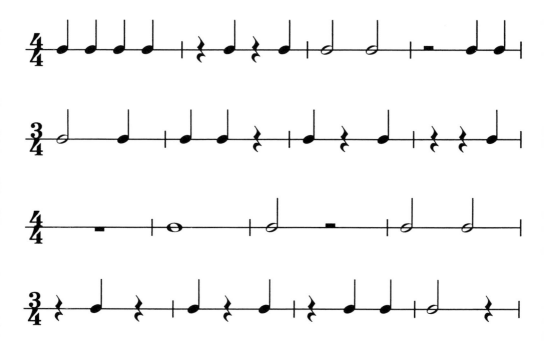

Date: /   /

Nothing can bring you peace but yourself.

Ralph Waldo Emerson

Practice writing the counts in the examples below:

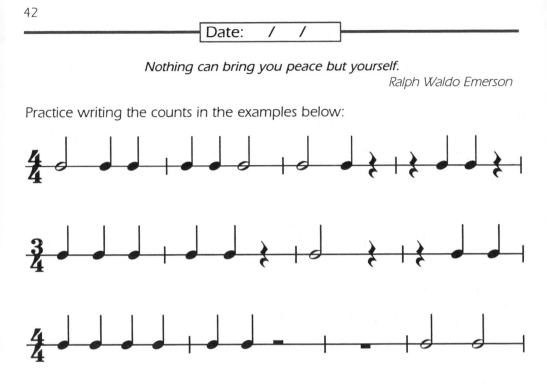

Write the NOTES and RESTS that represent the counts shown below:

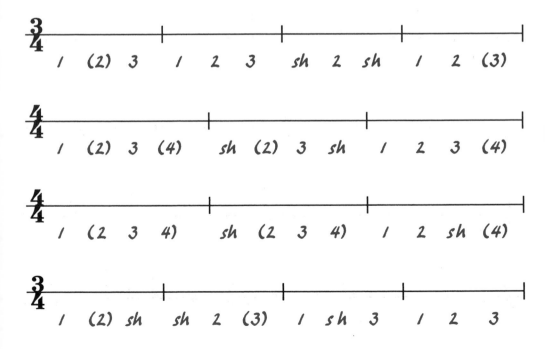

3/4

/ (2) 3   /   2   3   sh 2 sh   /   2 (3)

4/4

/ (2) 3 (4)   sh (2) 3 sh   /   2   3 (4)

4/4

/ (2 3 4)   sh (2 3 4)   /   2 sh (4)

3/4

/ (2) sh   sh 2 (3)   / sh 3   /   2   3

We listen to great music and know that all our joys and sorrows are part of something beyond our comprehension—and so infinitely valuable.

Jesse O'Neill

EIGHTH NOTES can be counted by dividing each beat in half. You can do this by saying the word "and" or writing the symbol "&" after the number.

For example:

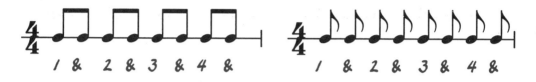

EIGHTH, QUARTER, HALF, and WHOLE NOTES can be combined to create rhythms like the following:

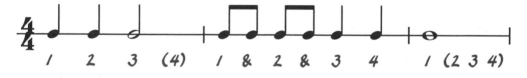

Write the counts for the examples shown below:

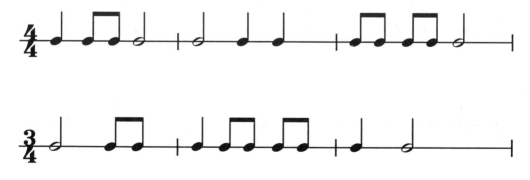

44

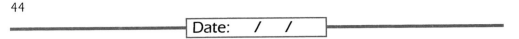
It's never too late to start over again.

Unknown

When counting EIGHTH RESTS, treat them the same as QUARTER, HALF, and WHOLE RESTS. Simply place the "**sh**" where it falls based on the rhythm indicated.

For Example:

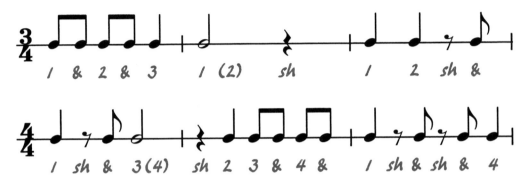

Write the counts for the examples shown below:

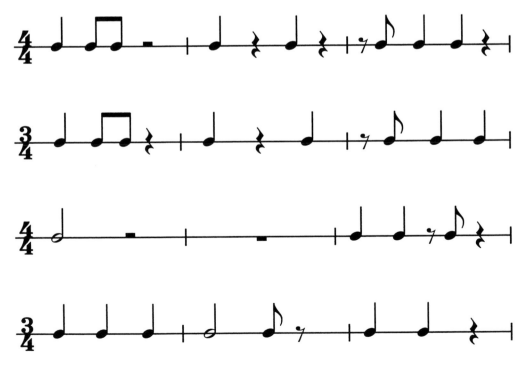

VM5S

Date: / /

Do not follow where the path may lead. Go instead where there is no path and leave a trail.

Unknown

Write the counts for the examples shown below:

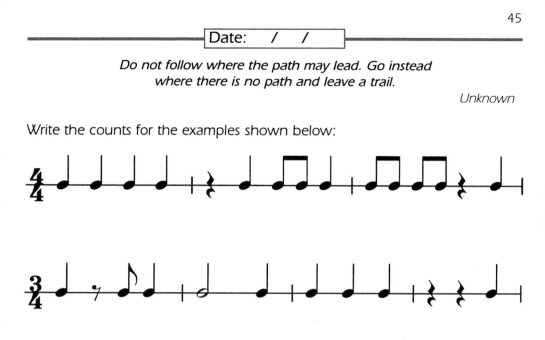

Write the NOTES and RESTS that represent the counts shown below:

Example:

Date: /   /

QUIZ 4 REVIEW

Write the correct counts for the rhythms shown below:

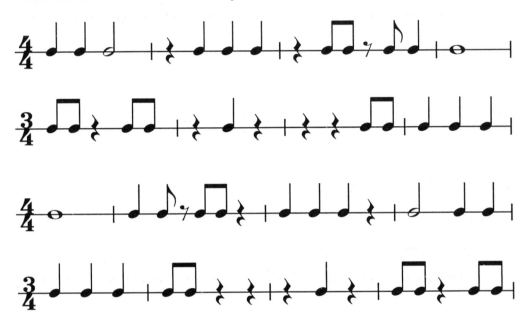

Write the NOTES and RESTS that represent the counts shown below:

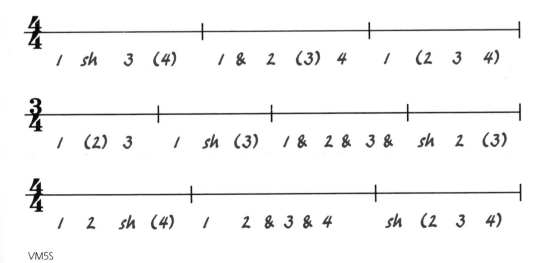

Unit 5

| Date: / / |

Music is the voice that tells us that the human race is greater than it knows.
Marion C. Garretty

A **DOT** may be added to a note to lengthen its rhythmic value. The DOT is equal to half of the original note value.

In $\frac{4}{4}$ time, a QUARTER NOTE equals one beat. By placing a DOT after the QUARTER NOTE, it equals one-and-a-half beats and looks like this:

♩.

Dotted Quarter Note = 1 beat + ½ beat (½ of 1 beat) = 1½ beats

In $\frac{4}{4}$ time, a HALF NOTE equals two beats. By placing a DOT after the HALF NOTE, it equals three beats and looks like this:

♩.

Dotted Half Note = 2 beats + 1 beat (½ of 2 beats) = 3 beats

Complete the examples shown below by adding the rhythms including DOTS:

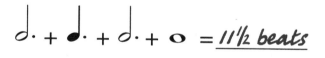

♩. + ♩. + ♩. + o = <u>*11½ beats*</u>

♩ + ♩. + ♩. + ♪ = _____

♪ + ♩. + ♩. + o = _____

♩ + ♩. + ♩. + o = _____

48

To accomplish great things, we must not only act,
but also dream; not only plan, but also believe.

Anatole France

Using the following examples of DOTTED RHYTHMS, notice how the numbers are placed to correctly count the rhythms:

Dotted Half Note

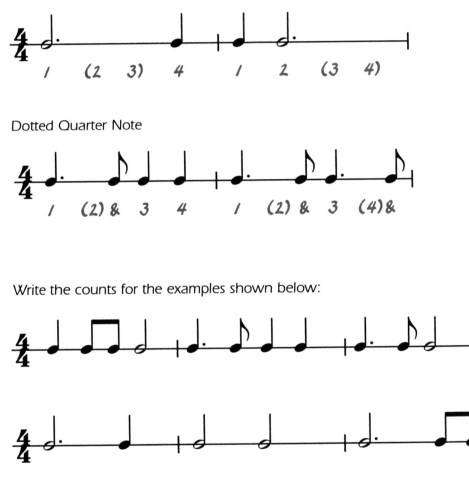

Write the counts for the examples shown below:

Date: / /

*The best portion of a good man's life are his little, nameless,
unremembered acts of kindness and of love.*

William Wordsworth

Write the counts for the examples shown below:

Now do the same in these examples including RESTS:

Example:

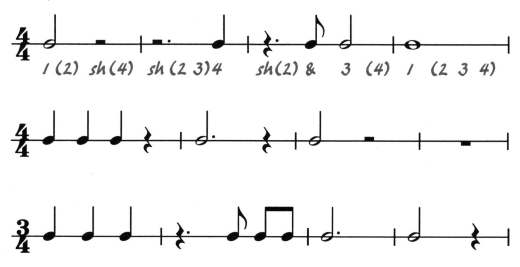

1 (2) sh (4) sh (2 3)4   sh(2) & 3 (4) / (2 3 4)

Date: /   /

Failure is the opportunity to begin again more intelligently.

Henry Ford

Another way to affect the duration of a given rhythm is by adding a TIE. A TIE is a curved line connecting two notes of the same pitch in which both note values are combined and held as one rhythmic duration.

TIES can go across BAR LINES, making it possible for notes to carry over from one MEASURE to another.

Example:

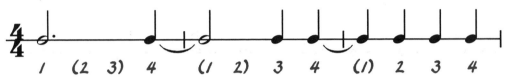

Write the counts for the examples shown below:

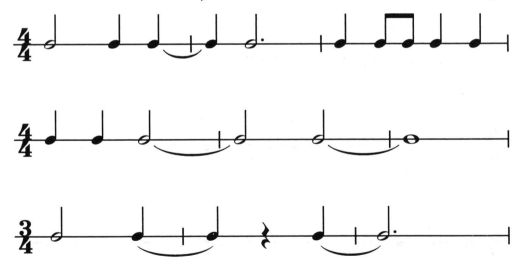

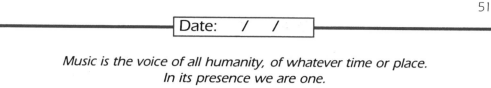

Music is the voice of all humanity, of whatever time or place.
In its presence we are one.

Charlotte Gray

Write the counts for the examples shown below:

Date: /   /

Insist on yourself; never imitate... Every great man is unique.
Ralph Waldo Emerson

Thus far you have learned rhythmic values in which the QUARTER NOTE receives one beat. This is not always the case. The EIGHTH NOTE can also receive one beat.

The TIME SIGNATURE $\frac{6}{8}$ tells us that there are six beats in each MEASURE and the EIGHTH NOTE receives one beat.

For example:

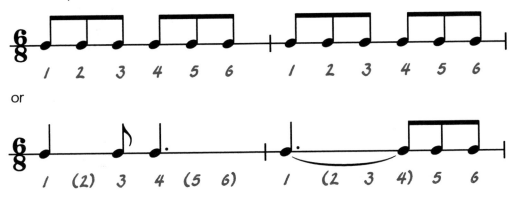

or

Write the counts for the example below. Remember, QUARTER NOTES now receive two beats!

Notice that the EIGHTH NOTES are grouped into threes:

This is true for the TIME SIGNATURES of $\frac{3}{8}$, $\frac{6}{8}$, and $\frac{9}{8}$.

Date: / /

*How is it that music can, without words, evoke our laughter,
our fears, our highest aspiration?*

Jane Swan

There can be any number of beats in a MEASURE, and any type of note can receive one beat.

Examples:

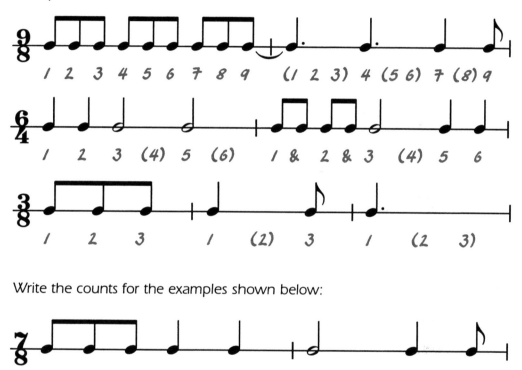

Write the counts for the examples shown below:

Write the NOTES that represent the counts shown below:

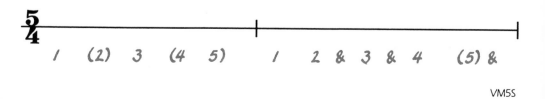

Date: /   /

And life is what we make it, always has been, always will be.

Grandma Moses

Write the counts for the examples shown below, paying close attention to the TIME SIGNATURE:

Date: / /

The difference between falling and failing is whether or not you choose to get up.

Unknown

Write the counts for the examples shown below:

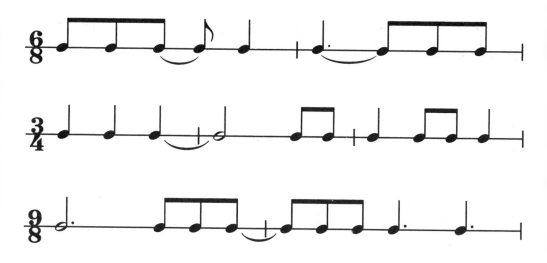

Write the NOTES that represent the counts shown below:

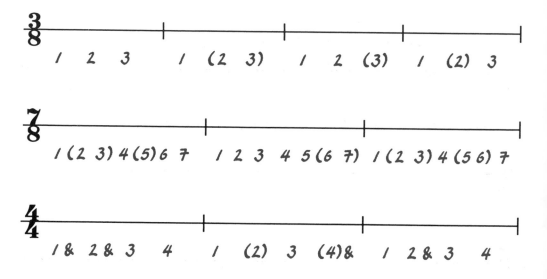

Date: / /

Most people are about as happy as they make up their minds to be.
Abraham Lincoln

Quiz 5 REVIEW

Write the counts for the examples shown below, paying close attention to the TIME SIGNATURES:

Write the NOTES and RESTS that represent the counts shown below:

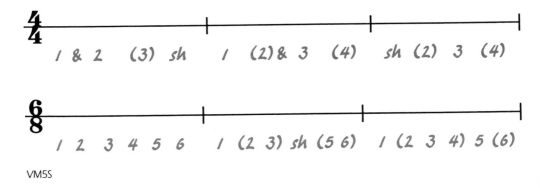

Unit 6

Date: /   /

*If someone thinks they have all the answers, it just means that
they haven't asked all the questions.*

Unknown

In music, songs can be placed higher or lower in pitch depending on the effect desired by the composer, the range of the voice or instrument, or the ease with which it may be played.

In order to establish how high or low a piece is performed, we use a KEY SIGNATURE. The KEY SIGNATURE is found at the beginning of each STAFF and is located to the right of the TREBLE and/or BASS CLEFS.

Write the definition of KEY SIGNATURE in your own words:

_____

_____

_____

Below is an example of a KEY SIGNATURE:

Silent Night by Kirby Shaw
©1989 Kirby Shaw Music
Used with permission 2005

Date: / /

You will find as you look back upon your life that the moments that stand out,
the moments when you have really lived, are the moments
when you have done things in the spirit of love.

Henry Drummond

A FLAT (♭) is used to lower any pitch by a half step.

FLATS are placed just to the left of the pitch which is to be lowered.

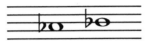

FLATS may also be used as part of the KEY SIGNATURE.

Write the definition of FLAT:

_____

Draw eight FLAT signs on the STAFF below:

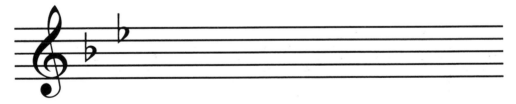

Make sure that the base of the FLAT is centered on the line or space of the given note.

Date: /   /

What lies behind us and what lies before us are tiny matters
compared to what lies within us.

Ralph Waldo Emerson

A SHARP (♯) is used to raise any pitch by a half step.

SHARPS are placed just to the left of the pitch which is to be raised.

SHARPS may also be used as part of the KEY SIGNATURE.

Write the definition of SHARP:

_____

Draw eight SHARP signs on the STAFF below:

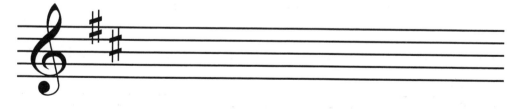

Make sure that the center of the SHARP surrounds the line or space of the given note.

You cannot teach a man anything; you can only
help him discover it within himself.

Galileo

The number of FLATS or SHARPS in the KEY SIGNATURE determines the KEY of the song.

If there are FLATS in the KEY SIGNATURE, they will always be placed in the following order: B E A D G C F. They will be placed from left to right on the staff as shown:

Write the order of FLATS: _____

The difference between what we do and what we are capable of doing
would suffice to solve most of the world's problems.

Mahatma Gandhi

Draw FLATS on the STAFF below in the order they appear in a KEY SIGNATURE:

Life is a song – sing it.
Life is a game – play it.
Life is a challenge – meet it.
Life is a dream – realize it.
Life is a sacrifice – offer it.
Life is love – enjoy it.

Sai Baba

If there are SHARPS in the KEY SIGNATURE, they will always be placed in the following order: F C G D A E B (the reverse order of FLATS) as shown:

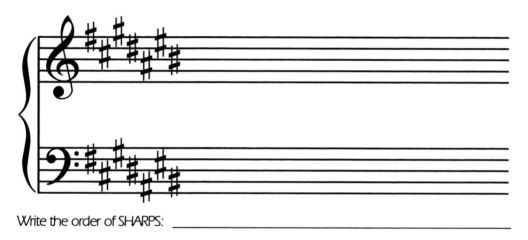

Write the order of SHARPS: _____

The best and most beautiful things in the world cannot be seen, nor touched . . . but are felt in the heart.

Helen Keller

Draw SHARPS on the STAFF below in the order that they appear in a KEY SIGNATURE:

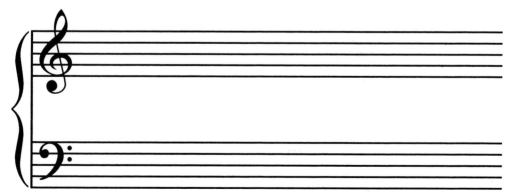

The heart of a fool is in his mouth, but the mouth of a wise man is in his heart.
Benjamin Franklin

QUIZ 6 REVIEW

Write the order of FLATS:

Write the order of SHARPS:

___ ___ ___ ___ ___ ___ ___

___ ___ ___ ___ ___ ___ ___

On the STAVES below, draw FLATS and SHARPS in the correct order:

FLATS

SHARPS

Unit 7

Date: / /

Life is an echo; what you send out will come back to you.
Unknown

There are various methods in determining the KEY of a song. If you already know a particular method, you may find that the following foolproof method takes your understanding of KEY SIGNATURES to a new level.

For singers who already know the solfége system, use the following method to find the KEY:

Your goal is always to find DO. When you find DO, you have found the KEY! (You may also use numbers instead of syllables.)

Your goal is to find _____.

In finding the syllable DO, you have found _____.

VM5S

Date: / /

When the power of love overcomes the love of power,
then there will be true peace.

Sri Chin Moi Gosh

When there are FLATS in the KEY SIGNATURE, locate the FLAT farthest to the right and call it FA. From there, go up or down the lines and spaces until you find DO. The letter name of the line or space that is DO is the KEY.

Circle the FLAT farthest to the right and write the word "FA" next to it:

Example:

Following the example shown below, count down from FA to find DO. Determine the letter name of the line or space of DO and write it in the space provided:

Example:

DO is:___**E**___   DO is:_____   DO is:_____

If the KEY SIGNATURE has more than one FLAT, you must include "flat (♭)" after the name of the KEY.

Example:

Key:___**E♭**___   Key:_____   Key:_____

VM5S

Date: / /

All truths are easy to understand once they are discovered;
the point is to discover them.

Galileo Galilei

Here are five easy steps to determine the KEY when the KEY SIGNATURE contains FLATS:

1. Locate the FLAT farthest to the right.

2. The FLAT on the right is always FA.

3. Count up or down the lines and spaces from FA to determine DO.

4. Determine the letter name of the line or space of DO.

5. Include "flat (♭)" if necessary.

Congratulations, you have found the KEY!

Determine the KEY for the following examples:

Key:_____   Key:_____   Key:_____

Key:_____   Key:_____   Key:_____

Oh, the worst of all tragedies is not to die young, but to live until I am seventy-five and yet not ever truly to have lived.

Rev. Dr. Martin Luther King, Jr.

When there are SHARPS in the KEY SIGNATURE, locate the SHARP farthest to the right, and call it TI. From there, simply go up to the next line or space to find DO. That is the KEY.

Circle the SHARP farthest to the right and write "TI" next to it:

Example:

Following the example shown below, find DO, which is up a line or space from TI. Determine the letter name of DO and write it in the space provided:

Example:

DO is: **D**   DO is:_____   DO is:_____

Once you have determined the letter name, check to see if there is a SHARP in the KEY SIGNATURE on the line or space that is DO. If there is, you must include "sharp (♯)" after the name of the KEY.

Example:

Key:___**D**___   Key:_____   Key:_____
No sharp
on D

Date: /   /

Recognize where you shine, and share that glow with the universe.

Unknown

Here are five easy steps to determine the KEY when the KEY SIGNATURE contains SHARPS:

1. Locate the SHARP farthest to the right.
2. The SHARP on the right is always TI.
3. Go up to the next line or space to find DO.
4. Determine the letter name of the line or space of DO.
5. Include "sharp (♯)" if necessary.

Congratulations, you have found the KEY!

Determine the KEY for the following examples:

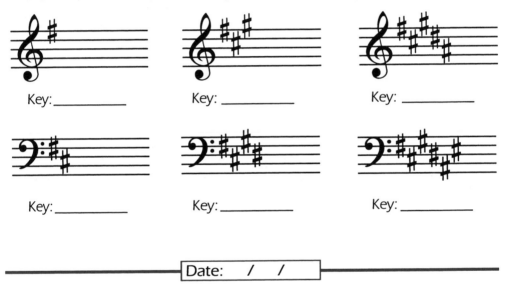

Key:_____

Key:_____

Key:_____

Key:_____

Key:_____

Key:_____

Date: /   /

Be kind, for everyone you meet is fighting a hard battle.

Plato

There is only one KEY that you have to memorize:

If there are NO SHARPS OR FLATS in the KEY SIGNATURE, the KEY is C.

Write the following sentence on the lines below:
If there are no sharps or flats in the key signature, it is the key of C.

_____

_____

You generate and strengthen self-esteem when you live with integrity, in harmony with your values. Commit yourself to them with all your heart.

Anonymous

For the exercises below, show your work to determine the Key:

Example:

Last flat is **FA**

Find **DO**
Do is on **E**

Flat on E

Check for flats in key signature
Key: **E flat**

Now you try:

Last flat is _____

Do is on _____

Key: _____

Last sharp is _____

Do is on _____

Key: _____

Last flat is _____

Do is on _____

Key: _____

Last sharp is _____

Do is on _____

Key: _____

VM5S

Date: /   /

Real understanding does not come from what we learn in books; it comes from what we learn from love of nature, of music, of man. For only what is learned in that way is truly understood.

Pablo Casals

Identify the KEY of each example below:

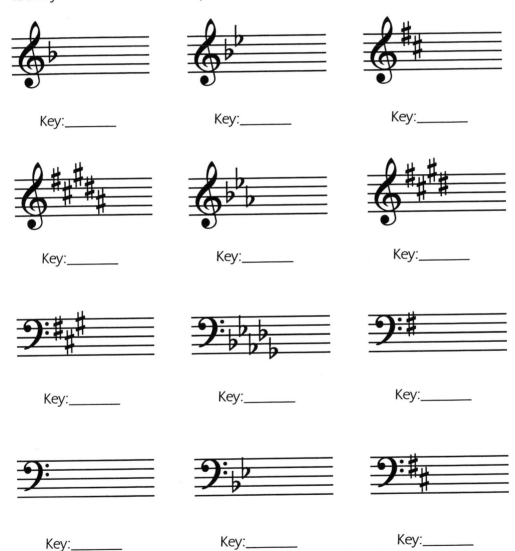

Key:_____

Key:_____

Key:_____

Key:_____

Key:_____

Key:_____

Key:_____

Key:_____

Key:_____

Key:_____

Key:_____

Key:_____

Date: /   /

The safest course is to do nothing against one's conscience. With this secret, we can enjoy life and have no fear from death.

Voltaire

QUIZ 7 REVIEW

Identify the KEY of each example below:

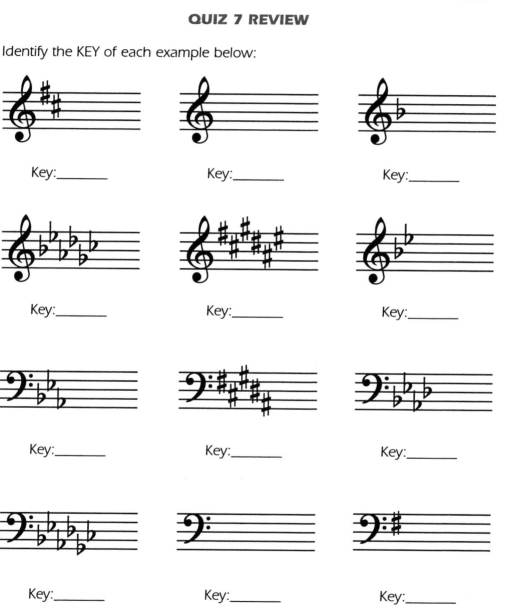

Key:_____

Key:_____

Key:_____

Key:_____

Key:_____

Key:_____

Key:_____

Key:_____

Key:_____

Key:_____

Key:_____

Key:_____

Unit 8

Date: / /

Put your heart, mind, intellect, and soul into your smallest acts.
This is the secret of success.

Sivananda Sarasvati

Every song has a KEY SIGNATURE. When there are no SHARPS or FLATS, there is still a KEY SIGNATURE—the Key of C. If there are SHARPS or FLATS in the KEY SIGNATURE, they must be applied to every note with the same name.

For example, in the KEY of E♭ there are three notes that are altered because of the KEY SIGNATURE. B becomes B♭, E becomes E♭, and A becomes A♭. All other notes will stay the same.

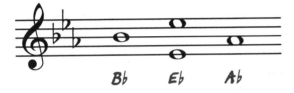

In the Key of D there are two notes that will be altered because of the KEY SIGNATURE. F becomes F♯ and C becomes C♯. All other notes will stay the same.

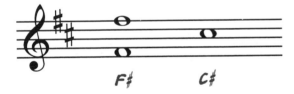

Based on the KEY SIGNATURES shown, name each note:

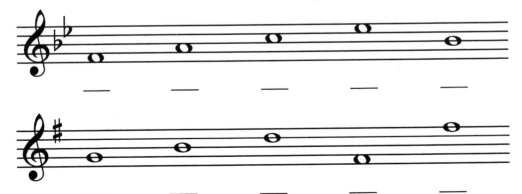

We must become the change we want to see.

Mahatma Gandhi

A Natural (♮) is used to cancel a SHARP or a FLAT within a measure.

Example:

B flat becomes B natural

Notice that NATURALS are placed just to the left of the pitch which is to be changed.

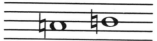

Write the definition of NATURAL:

_____

Draw eight NATURAL signs on the STAFF below:

Make sure that the NATURAL is centered
on the line or space of the given note.

VM5S

Date: / /

Where words leave off, music begins.

Heinrich Heine

A NATURAL cancels only those notes of same pitch that occur up to the BAR LINE. Once a new MEASURE has begun, the NATURAL no longer applies.

Example:

F   G   Ab   G   Ab   G   A♮   A♮   F   G   Ab

Write the correct note name below each pitch:

73

Date: /   /

Just don't give up trying to do what you really want to do . . .
where there's love and inspiration, I don't think you can go wrong.

Ella Fitzgerald

Write the names of the notes in the spaces provided:

74

Date: / /

He that is slow to anger is better than the mighty; and he that ruleth his spirit than he that taketh a city.

Proverbs 16:32b

QUIZ 8 REVIEW

Write the names of the notes in the spaces provided:

VM5S

Unit 9

| Date: / / |

Failure is an event, not a person.

Unknown

DYNAMICS are symbols or words that are used to give music a more expressive feeling. They determine the volume at which the music is to be played or sung.

Using your own words, define the word DYNAMICS:

_____

_____

| Date: / / |

We see things not as they are, but as we are.

Talmud

Three DYNAMICS that mean *to sing or play softly* are MEZZO PIANO (*mp*), PIANO (*p*), and PIANISSIMO (*pp*).

MEZZO PIANO means *moderately soft* and can be identified by the abbreviation *mp*. Mezzo is an Italian word, pronounced "mehtzo."

PIANO means *soft* and can be identified by the abbreviation *p*.

PIANISSIMO means *very soft* and can be identified by the abbreviation *pp*.

How loud should you sing when you see *pp*? _____

How loud should you sing when you see *mp*? _____

How loud should you sing when you see *p*? _____

Note: The Slabbinck definition of *piano* for choral singers is half the volume, twice the intensity.

Date: /   /

Don't be afraid to take a big step if one is indicated.
You can't cross a chasm in two small jumps.

David Lloyd George

Three DYNAMIC markings that mean *to play or sing loudly* are MEZZO FORTE (*mf*), FORTE (*f*), and FORTISSIMO (*ff*).

MEZZO FORTE means *moderately loud* and can be identified by the abbreviation *mf*.

FORTE means *loud* and can be identified by the abbreviation *f*.

FORTISSIMO means *very loud*, and can be identified by the abbreviation *ff*.

How loud should you sing when you see *ff* ? _____

How loud should you sing when you see *mf* ? _____

How loud should you sing when you see *f* ? _____

Date: /   /

Ignorance never settles a question.

Benjamin Disraeli

CRESCENDO is a DYNAMIC marking that means *to gradually get louder*. It is represented by the symbol ⎯⎯⎯⎯⎯⎯ or by the abbreviation *cresc.*

Write the definition of CRESCENDO:

_____

_____

Draw the symbol and abbreviation for CRESCENDO:

Symbol _____

Abbreviation _____

Date: / /

*Never discourage anyone...who continually makes
progress, no matter how slow.*

Plato

DECRESCENDO is a DYNAMIC marking that means *to gradually get softer.* It is
represented by the symbol ⟩ or by the abbreviation *decresc.*

Write the definition for DECRESCENDO:

_____

_____

Draw the symbol and abbreviation for DECRESCENDO:

Symbol _____

Abbreviation _____

Date: / /

Education is the best provision for the journey to old age.

Aristotle

DIMINUENDO is another DYNAMIC marking that means *to gradually get softer.*
It is represented by the abbreviation *dim.*

Write the definition of DIMINUENDO:

_____

_____

DIMINUENDO may be abbreviated as _____.

Draw the symbol and both abbreviations that indicate to gradually get softer:

Symbol _____

Abbreviations _____ or _____

78

Date:	/	/

Every child is an artist. The problem is how to remain an artist once he grows up.
Pablo Picasso

RITARDANDO is a term that means *to gradually get slower.* It is represented by the abbreviation *rit.* or *ritard.*

Write the definition of RITARDANDO:

_____

RITARDANDO may be abbreviated as _____ or _____.

Date:	/	/

The future belongs to those who believe in the beauty of their dreams.
Eleanor Roosevelt

RALLENTANDO is another term that means *to gradually get slower.* It is represented by the abbreviation *rall.*

Write the definition of RALLENTANDO:

_____

RALLENTANDO may be abbreviated as _____.

ACCELERANDO is a music term that means *to gradually get faster.* It is represented by the abbreviation *accel.*

Write the definition of ACCELERANDO:

_____

ACCELERANDO can be abbreviated as _____ .

Date: /   /

*Do not go where the path may lead, go instead
where there is no path and leave a trail.*

Ralph Waldo Emerson

Match each term to its correct definition:

___ forte   a. gradually get softer

___ piano   b. gradually get slower

___ mezzo forte   c. gradually get faster

___ fortissimo   d. loud

___ mezzo piano   e. gradually get louder

___ pianissimo   f. medium loud

___ crescendo   g. medium soft

___ decrescendo   h. gradually get slower

___ diminuendo   i. gradually get softer

___ ritardando   j. soft

___ rallentando   k. very soft

___ accelerando   l. very loud

Date: /   /

Life is a succession of lessons which must be lived to be understood.

Helen Keller

A FERMATA is a symbol that means *to hold a certain note longer than its defined value.* The duration of the held note is generally determined by the conductor.

A FERMATA looks like 𝅘𝅥 or 𝄐.

Write the definition of FERMATA:

_____

_____

Draw a FERMATA: _____ or _____

Look at the following musical excerpt. Draw FERMATAS above the last NOTES and REST:

Silent Night by Kirby Shaw
©1989 Kirby Shaw Music
Used with permission 2005

Keep away from people who try to belittle your ambitions. Small people always do that, but the really great make you feel that you, too, can become great.

Mark Twain

LEGATO is a music term that means *to be played or sung in a smooth and connected manner.* It is indicated by an arched line connecting two or more notes together.

Write the definition of LEGATO:

_____

_____

An example of LEGATO is shown below:

Silent Night by Kirby Shaw
©1989 Kirby Shaw Music
Used with permission 2005

Describe how LEGATO marks are indicated:

_____

_____

| Date: / / |

*Seek out friends who recognize your goodness and
who lovingly affirm your worth.*

Anonymous

STACCATO is a music term that means *to play or sing in a short, detached manner*. It is indicated by a DOT placed directly above or below the notes to be affected.

Write the definition of STACCATO:

_____

_____

Staccato markings look like this:

Describe how STACCATO marks are indicated:

_____

_____

Date: /   /

*To listen closely and reply well is the highest perfection we are
able to attain in the art of conversation.*

Francois de La Rochefoucald

D.C. AL FINE (feen-ā) is a marking that tells the musician to return to the
beginning of the piece and play or sing until the word *Fine*.

D.C. is the abbreviation for *da capo*, which is Italian for "the top."

Write the definition of **D.C. al Fine**:

_____

_____

This is an example of **D.C. al Fine**:

1. Sing the first and second lines, until you reach **D.C. al Fine**.
2. Go back to *da capo* (the beginning).
3. Sing until you reach **Fine** (the end).

Date: / /

Keep challenging yourself to grow, even when that means you could fail.
Anonymous

D.S. AL CODA is a marking that tells the musician to return to the ※ sign, continue until reaching the ⊕ symbol, and then "jump" to the same ⊕ symbol near the end of the piece.

D.S. is the abbreviation for *dal segno*, which means "the sign."
The last section with the ⊕ symbol is called a *Coda*.

Write the definition of **D.S. al Coda**:

_____

_____

Draw the sign for D.S.: _____ Draw the sign for CODA: _____.

The following is an example of how to follow the signs in the music score:

1. Sing lines one, two, and three, until you reach **D.S. al Coda**.
2. From the **D.S. al Coda** at the end of line three, go to the beginning of line two (※).
3. Sing line two.
4. Skip from the CODA symbol at the end of line two (⊕) to the CODA symbol (⊕)at the beginning of line four.
5. Sing line four.

| Date: / / |

No one is useless in this world who lightens the burdens of another.

Charles Dickens

A REPEAT SIGN tells the musician to repeat a group of measures.

Below are examples of how REPEAT SIGNS are used. Notice that the two dots in the REPEAT SIGN are placed on either side of the third line.

If the passage is to be repeated from the very beginning the only dots will be at the end of the section to be repeated.

If the section to be repeated is somewhere after the beginning, look for the dots that are on the right side of a double bar. These indicate the beginning of the section that is to be repeated.

In the example below, insert REPEAT SIGNS in the middle and at the end of the phrase:

Reminder:
If there is no ‖: you go back to the very beginning from :‖.

Date: /   /

Believe that with your feelings and your work you are taking part in the greatest; the more strongly you cultivate this belief, the more will reality and the world go forth from it.

Rainer Maria Rilke

Sometimes a passage of music will need to be repeated with a different ending the second time. In this case, the musician follows the REPEAT SIGNS as written, but the second time through, the musician skips the measure(s) in the FIRST ENDING $\boxed{1.}$ and proceeds to the measure(s) in the SECOND ENDING $\boxed{2.}$.

The following is an example of music with FIRST & SECOND ENDINGS:

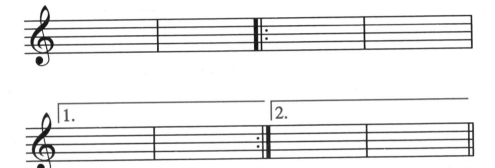

1. Sing until you reach 𝄇.

2. Go back to 𝄆 and sing to the end of the first line.

3. Jump to $\boxed{2.}$ and sing to the end of the second line.

Insert REPEAT SIGNS and FIRST & SECOND ENDINGS as shown in the above example:

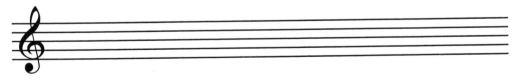

Date: / /

Those who dare to fail miserably can achieve greatly.

Robert F. Kennedy

QUIZ 9 REVIEW

Match the following terms with their definitions:

_____ mezzo piano (*mp*)   a. gradually get softer

_____ piano (*p*)   b. hold until the conductor cuts you off

_____ pianissimo (*pp*)   c. sung the first time through a repeat

_____ mezzo forte (*mf*)   d. medium soft

_____ forte (*f*)   e. gradually get faster

_____ fortissimo (*ff*)   f. repeat material between these two signs

_____ crescendo   g. very loud

_____ decrescendo   h. short and detached

_____ diminuendo   i. gradually get slower

_____ accelerando   j. gradually get louder

_____ ritardando   k. soft

_____ rallentando   l. smooth and connected

_____ fermata   m. sung the second time through a repeat

_____ staccato   n. the last section, designated by the ✛ symbol

_____ legato   o. very soft

_____ D.S. al Coda   p. gradually get slower

_____ coda   q. gradually get softer

_____ D.C. al Fine   r. loud

_____ ‖: :‖   s. medium loud

_____ |1.   t. instructs singer to go back to the beginning *(da capo)*

_____ |2.   u. instructs singer to return to the 𝄋 sign *(dal segno)* and sing until the ✛ symbol

Date: /   /

Truly to sing, that is a different breath.

Rainer Maria Rilke

FINAL EXAM REVIEW

Write the correct letter name below each note:

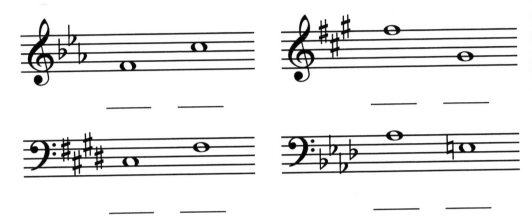

Write the counts for the excercises shown below:

Determine the KEY for the following examples:

Key:_____   Key:_____   Key:_____   Key:_____

(Continued on the next page)

Define the following terms:

mezzo piano (*mp*)_____

piano (*p*) _____

pianissimo (*pp*)_____

mezzo forte (*mf*) _____

forte (*f*)_____

fortissimo (*ff*) _____

crescendo _____

    is abbreviated as: _____and its symbol is:_____

decrescendo _____

    is abbreviated as: _____and its symbol is:_____

diminuendo _____

    is abbreviated as: _____and its symbol is:_____

accelerando _____

    is abbreviated as: _____

ritardando _____

    is abbreviated as: _____or _____

rallentando _____

    is abbreviated as: _____

fermata _____

    its symbol is: _____

(Continued on the next page)

90

Draw a LEGATO marking from the first note to the fourth note in the example below:

The definition of legato is: _____.

Draw STACCATO markings under the first four notes in the example below:

The definition of staccato is: _____

Fill in the blanks at the bottom of the page to describe the order in which the following STAVES should be sung:

1. Sing lines _____ through _____ .

2. At the end of line _____, go back to _____.

3. Sing from this point to _____ .

4. Skip from _____ to line _____ .

5 Sing from this point to _____ .

VM5S

Notes

GLOSSARY

TERM	SYMBOL	MEANING
Accelerando	*accel.*	to gradually get faster
Alto	A	the second highest voice in the choir
Bar Line		separates music into measures
Bass	B	the lowest voice in the choir
Bass Clef	𝄢	also known as F Clef; generally designates those notes that are lower in pitch
Clef	𝄞𝄢	a symbol that helps to identify musical notes and pitches
Crescendo	*cresc.* or <	to gradually get louder
D.C. al Fine		tells the musician to return to the beginning of the piece and play or sing until the word *Fine*; D.C. abbreviates *da capo*
D.S. al Coda		tells the musician to return to 𝄋 (*dal segno*), and continue until ⊕ (*coda*)
Decrescendo	*decresc.* or >	to gradually get softer
Diminuendo	*dim.* or >	to gradually get softer
Dotted Note	♩. ♪.	a dot lengthens the value of a note by half of its original value
Dynamics		symbols or words that determine the volume at which the music is to be played or sung
Fermata	‿ ⌢	indicates to hold a certain note longer than its defined value; the duration is generally determined by the conductor
First Ending	1	contains material to be sung the first time through a repeated passage
Flat	♭	lowers any pitch by a half step
Forte	*f*	loud
Fortissimo	*ff*	very loud

TERM	SYMBOL	MEANING
Grand Staff		a combination of the Treble Clef and Bass Clef; clefs are linked together with a brace
Key Signature		a group of sharp or flat signs that indicates the Key of the music that follows; helps establish how high or low a piece is performed
Legato		to play or sing in a smooth, connected manner; notes that are to be sung legato are connected by an arched line
Measure		the space within a Staff contained between two bar lines
Mezzo Forte	*mf*	moderately loud
Mezzo Piano	*mp*	moderately soft
Natural	♮	used to cancel a sharp or flat within a measure
Note	o ♩ ♪ ♩	symbol that represents the length of sound
Pianissimo	*pp*	very soft
Piano	*p*	soft
Rallentando	*rall.*	to gradually get slower
Repeat Sign	or	tells the musician to repeat a group of measures
Rest		symbol that represents the length of silence
Ritardando	*rit.* or *ritard.*	to gradually get slower
Second Ending	2	contains material to be sung the second time through a repeat
Sharp	♯	raises any pitch by a half step
Soprano	S	the highest voice in the choir
Staccato	♩ ♩	to play or sing in a short, detached manner; a staccato note is indicated by a dot placed directly above or below it
Staff		a group of five equally spaced horizontal lines upon which music is written

94

TERM	SYMBOL	MEANING
Tenor	T	the second lowest voice in the choir
Tie		a curved line connecting two notes of the same pitch in which both note values are combined and held as one rhythmic duration
Time Signature		indicates how many beats occur in each measure
Treble Clef		also known as G Clef; generally designates those notes that are higher in pitch

Use this bookmark to quickly find your place at the start of each rehearsal!

One-Minute Theory

by Ronald Slabbinck
and Holly Shaw-Slabbinck

kjos